P9-DNR-166

Count My Blessings

1 Through 10

This book
belongs to

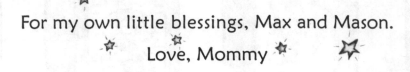

For my own little blessings, Max and Mason.
Love, Mommy

No part of this publication may be reproduced, stored in a retrieval system,
or transmitted in any form or by any means, electronic, mechanical, photocopying,
recording, or otherwise, without written permission of the publisher. For information regarding permission,
write to G. P. Putnam's Sons, a division of Penguin Young Readers Group, a member of
Penguin Group (USA) Inc., 345 Hudson Street, New York, NY 10014.

ISBN-13: 978-0-545-05420-1
ISBN-10: 0-545-05420-6

Copyright © 2006 by Salina Yoon.
All rights reserved. Published by Scholastic Inc., 557 Broadway, New York, NY 10012,
by arrangement with G. P. Putnam's Sons, a division of Penguin Young Readers Group, a member of
Penguin Group (USA) Inc. SCHOLASTIC and associated logos are trademarks and/or registered trademarks of Scholastic Inc.

12 11 10 9 8   10 11 12 13 14/0

Printed in the U.S.A.   40

First Scholastic printing, November 2007

Design by Gunta Alexander

Text set in Maiandra

Count My Blessings

1 Through 10

Salina Yoon

SCHOLASTIC INC.
New York Toronto London Auckland Sydney
Mexico City New Delhi Hong Kong Buenos Aires

1 house

Bless this home for my family.

 **parents**

Bless Mother and Father for loving me.

 **3** **friends**

Bless my friends, both old and new.

Act 1
Lost in Space

4 pets

Bless my pets, so dear to me too.

5 stuffed animals

Bless my stuffed animals—to sleep,
I will take.

birds

Bless the birds that call me to wake.

7 butterflies

Bless the butterflies that flutter above.

 **cookies**

Bless the cookies that are baked with love.

 **squares**

Bless each square on Grandmother's quilt.

10 wooden toys

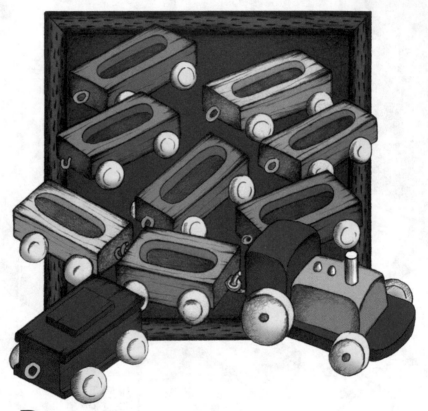

Bless the wooden toys that
Grandfather built.

I count my blessings,
one through ten.
Keep us safe, I pray.

Amen.

A Bedtime Prayer

Bless this home for my family.

Bless Mother and Father for loving me.

Bless my friends, both old and new.

Bless my pets, so dear to me too.

Bless my stuffed animals—to sleep, I will take.

Bless the birds that call me to wake.

Bless the butterflies that flutter above.

Bless the cookies that are baked with love.

Bless each square on Grandmother's quilt.

Bless the wooden toys that Grandfather built.

I count my blessings, one through ten.

Keep us safe, I pray. Amen.